Team Challenges

40 Divergent Thinking Activities

creativity

problem-solving

teamwork

cooperation

strategic thinking

performance

Charlotte Samiec

Editor: Margaret Maher
Book and cover design: Susana Siew-Demunck

Published in Australia by

HAWKER BROWNLOW
•
E D U C A T I O N

P.O. Box 580, Moorabbin,
Victoria 3189, Australia
Phone: (03) 9555 1344 Fax: (03) 9553 4538
Toll Free Ph: 1800 33 4603 Fax: 1800 15 0445
Website: http://www.hbe.com.au
Email: orders@hbe.com.au

© 2004 Hawker Brownlow Education
Printed in Australia

Code: HB3542

National Library of Australia Cataloguing-in-Publication entry:

  Samiec, Charlotte.
  Team challenges.

  ISBN 1 74101 354 2.

  1. Social groups – Problems, exercises, etc. I. Title.

  302.34

Contents

Contents

Introduction

What are 'team challenges'?

Team challenges are exciting, open-ended tasks that require teamwork, imagination and fast thinking to accomplish.

Who are team challenges for?

Team challenges can be used by teams of all kinds and in any situation where creativity and teamwork are valued. Teams should consist of between four and seven members. A team this size is big enough to benefit from the wide variety of ideas and talents of its members yet small enough to ensure that everyone is actively involved.

In an educational setting, team challenges are ideal for enrichment, extension and team-building purposes and in training students for competitions such as Tournament of the Minds, Odyssey of the Mind and Future Problem Solving. Team challenges are not restricted to school situations, however. They can be used by businesses, youth groups, scout groups, summer camps, senior-citizens' groups or rowing teams, just to name a few! Team challenges are lively and original tasks to get teams bonding. They are for anyone who is game!

Why should I use team challenges?

Team challenges are designed to be demanding but fun; to enhance cooperation, creativity, risk-taking, and higher-level thinking skills. Participating in the challenges will help team members strike out of tired, routine ways of thinking and make creative leaps into the unusual and untried. However, as in most real-life enterprises, solitary genius is not sufficient – to be successful, a team will need to spend time listening to everyone's ideas and utilise each member's talents.

Teams will be required to produce lots of ideas quickly – this ability to brainstorm at supersonic speeds often leads to real gems. As Linus Pauling said, 'The best way to have a good idea is to have lots of ideas.'

How the solutions and ideas are presented is important too. Many of the challenges call for teams to find imaginative ways to express their thoughts and inventions – they may never have tried opera before but …

In summary, the skills, teamwork and ways of thinking encountered in team challenges can flow into and be of benefit in the everyday world of work, home, school and community.

How are team challenges designed to be used?

Team challenges are clearly written and are meant to be read aloud to competing teams. A list of simple materials and a score sheet for the judges is provided with each challenge.

Most tasks take around ten minutes to complete but specific time limits and other restrictions are explained in each challenge. Rules, time limits, the ensuing tiny sense of panic and the need to score add to the fun of the challenge – imagine the lack of excitement in a football game if the score or rules were

not important! Restrictions and time limits also help keep teams on task and ensure that each member's skills and talents are utilised. One could spend all day working on a problem, but it takes teamwork and clear thinking to achieve the same goal in ten minutes.

The challenges are meant to be judged – warmly and encouragingly, of course, but still judged. This aspect, like the restrictions, gives a sense of purpose to the endeavour. What exactly is being judged and how to score points is explained in each challenge. A premium is always placed on teamwork.

Of course the challenges can be adapted to suit your own teams and purposes by altering the restrictions, changing the subject to a topic studied in class, a major world event, your company's clientele, shared experiences or a particular competition.

The challenges are not intended to be watched by an audience, especially not an audience of other teams that are about to tackle the same task. There may be benefit, however, in winning teams 'performing' their solutions after the event or the judges sharing what worked with all competing teams at the end of the competition. To help with this, the 'comments' section of the mark sheet provides a space for the judges to record general comments about each team's performance. Certainly there should be some feedback – either written or spoken – to teams about how they went.

A word about warming up

The challenges in this book are rigorous and will usually require some prior practice in problem solving, creativity and cooperation. There are many good resources readily available that provide ways of practising these skills. I have included a section of warm-ups to give an idea of the kind of exercises that may help individuals and teams hone these skills in preparation for team challenges.

The challenges in this book have been tried and tested with many teams over a number of years. I hope that your teams enjoy them too.

Charlotte Samiec

Suggested resources

Suid, Murray (2003). *Thinking Start-ups: Independent Study Cards Years 3–6*. Melbourne: Hawker Brownlow Education.

Ellis, L. Julie (2004). *CPS: A User's Guide. A Handbook of Creative Problem Solving Techniques*. Melbourne: Hawker Brownlow Education.

Reid, Lorene (1993). *Thinking Skills Resource Book*. Melbourne: Hawker Brownlow Education.

Johnson, L. Nancy (1993). *Questioning Makes the Difference*. Melbourne: Hawker Brownlow Education.

Marcus, A. Susan & McDonald, Penny (1991). *Tools for the Co-operative Classroom*. Melbourne: Hawker Brownlow Education.

Fligor, Marty (1993). *Brain Storming: The Book of Topics*. Melbourne: Hawker Brownlow Education.

The format of the challenges

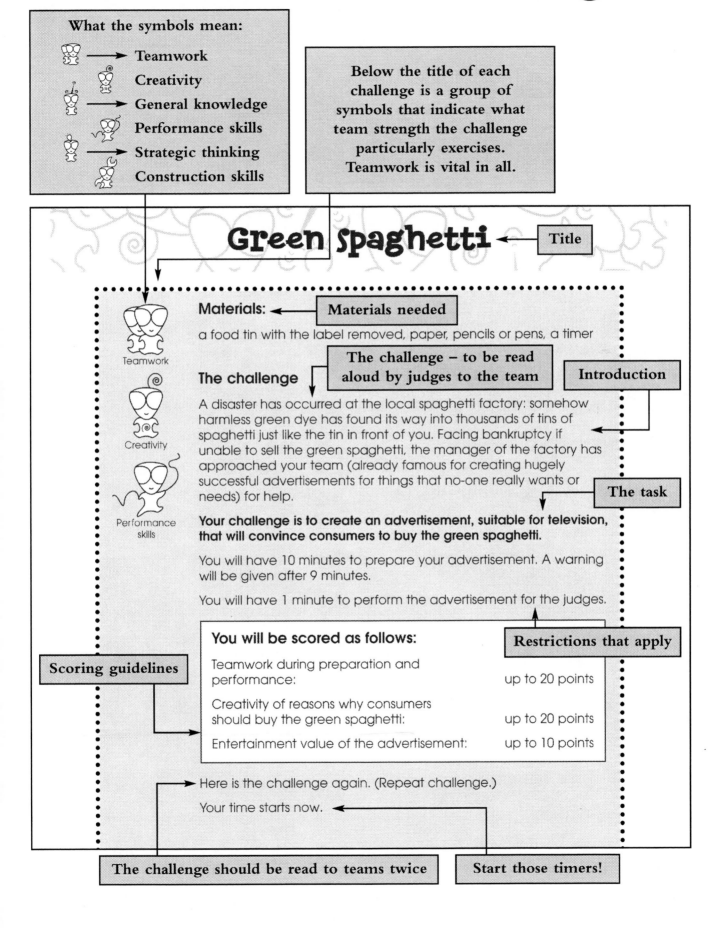

Tips for judges

- Think about the challenge ahead of time – perhaps make a list of expected and obvious responses so that you can appreciate truly original gems when teams are able to produce them.

- Many points are scored for creativity – be careful that an idea you mark high as 'very creative' the first time you hear it gets the same mark when you have heard it ten times.

- Look out for all those little indicators that team members are cooperating and being considerate of each other. Are they listening to everyone's ideas? Taking turns? Drawing out the quiet ones to give their opinions? Smiling? Laughing? Giving each other positive reinforcement?

- All teams will look to you for feedback about how they went – don't forget to ask them first what they thought about their performance. They probably have a good idea already and it is helpful for them to analyse what worked and what did not.

If there is more than one judge

- It is important to discuss the challenge beforehand. Agree on what kind of performance you would expect from teams to score well. For example, what would a team need to do to score 10 out of 10 for teamwork?

- If there are a number of teams competing it is helpful to make time after the first one or two performances to reassess expectations and scoring. Extra moderation may be needed according to the number of teams.

- It may be helpful for individual judges to focus on one element of the challenge and be responsible for judging, scoring and giving feedback for that aspect only.

Tips for teams

- You may have been in situations or competitions before where you were successful because of your individual strengths and talents. While those strengths and talents are still important, the judges will be looking to see how well you function as a team. So show the judges how well you work together:

  - listen to each other

  - encourage one another ('That's a good idea')

  - ask quieter members for their ideas

  - divide tasks up when you can

  - take turns

  - smile

  - laugh

  - and remember, NO put-downs.

- You are being 'judged' from the moment the judges first meet you until the moment you leave the room. The judges will appreciate being greeted politely, having your full attention while they are reading the challenge to you and being able to see and hear you clearly at all times. Don't forget to clean up after yourselves and thank the judges for their time.

- Make careful note of how the points are allocated and spend your time working on what counts. For example, if only 5 per cent of the marks are for performance skills, don't spend all your preparation time working on your dramatic entrance!

- Consider assigning roles. Having predetermined jobs such as 'scribe' and 'timekeeper' may help you work efficiently.

- How will you handle differences of opinion? Voting will probably go down well with the judges.

- Be careful of making comments that might be seen as racist or sexist – you will lose points for such conduct. Steer away from 'toilet' humour – it is unlikely to work in your favour.

- Spend time brainstorming ideas before you decide on a particular course of action. 'The best way to have a good idea is to have lots of ideas.' The first idea you have will probably be most other people's first idea too – keep thinking and something better will emerge.

- Keep your sense of humour and enjoy yourselves.

Warm-ups

These activities are examples of quick exercises to help develop creative, fluent thinking and teamwork. Team members will benefit from trying these kinds of activities as a way of training for team challenges. There are many good resources available with additional ideas – this is just a small sampler.

Speed builders

Do these speed builders as fast as you can around the circle, missing no-one.

Easy

Count up to 100	Pass a Mexican wave
Count backwards from 100 to zero	Toss a beanbag or ball
Say the alphabet	Unroll and reroll a roll of toilet paper

Name things:	**Name:**	**List alphabetically:**
that are red	famous people	animals
with holes in them	movie titles	foods
that are up	book titles	adjectives
with wheels	parts of the body	cities
with windows	animals	fantasy creatures
in the kitchen		cartoon characters
in the school		things in a science lab
in the circus		boys' names
with curves		sports
with corners		forms of transport
		objects in the room

Harder

Say the alphabet backwards	Blindfolded, pass around a handful of marbles	Calculate multiples of 13

Name:	**Describe uses for:**
emotions	a rubber band
song or movie titles with the word 'you' in them	a paddling pool
ways to get to school or work	a stopped clock
ways of carrying water	extracted teeth
proverbs	jigsaw-puzzle pieces
things to cut with	
opposites	
expressions containing the word 'good' (for example 'Good grief')	
euphemisms for death	
things worth photographing	
famous mysteries	
things that should be painted on buildings	

Explain what this is a picture of:

(Show teams an abstract picture, a simple doodle, a silhouette or an obscure magnified object.)

What do these things have in common?

Think up as many similarities as you can.

Easy	**Harder**	
The sun and the moon	A saucepan and a cloud	A few minutes discussion time can be given for these warm-ups. Answers could be written down or spoken as in the previous circle activities.
A tree and a castle	Sand and an argument	
A river and a song	A wedding and a storm	
Water and words	A pie and a headache	
A clock and a car	A tourist and a sandwich	

Give reasons why:

An elephant is in the classroom/office

A gigantic hole has appeared in the footpath overnight

Scientists in protective gear have just entered the building

All workers/students have been given the day off

Christmas presents are banned this Christmas

All men have just become unemployed

All public transport drivers are wearing pink hats

It's still dark at noon

Mr Noah next door has started building an ark

The letter *d* is eliminated from the alphabet

The sky is red

Angels have been seen on street corners

The prime minister has just resigned

Everyone is happy

Peace has broken out all over the world

There are children with green faces on the news

Tourists are flocking to the desert

String has sold out in all the shops

There is a giant pile of spaghetti on the steps of parliament house

They had to close the zoo

Your boss is wearing a tutu

Diamonds have lost all their value

Everyone has been issued with a balloon

The Internet doesn't work

Leprechauns are in the lift

Aeroplanes are all grounded

All the clocks have stopped

One-minute wonders

Many of the following warm-ups require team members to get up and move.

Teams have one minute to:

become a volcano and erupt

become a train/boat/car/bike and transport a team member across the room

become the machine at the centre of the universe

become a photocopier and photocopy one of your team members

become a postcard from Egypt/Paris/London

become a troubled digestive system and create a burp

Two-minute wonders

Teams have two minutes to:

Make the longest span possible out of eight sheets of newspaper

Transport as much water as possible from one bucket to another 5 metres apart using only a cup. (Once in position no team member is allowed to move their legs.)

Act out the condensed history of the world

Make an anagram of team challenges

Draw a recognisable portrait of each team member

Compose a rhyming poem about a pair of trousers

Pass around the circle as many times as they can:

      a carrot using knees only

      a balloon using knees only

      a lifesaver lolly using toothpicks held between the teeth

      two balls – one clockwise and one anticlockwise

      a handful of wet spaghetti without dropping any

Come up with three imaginative names for:

      a gym

      a panel beater's workshop

      a novel about vegetables that take over the world

      a magazine about sports injuries

      an Internet site about pimples

      the gap between the big toe and the next toe

      the condition where you get a tune stuck in your head

      the fear of refrigerators

      the tendency to waste time on the Internet

      the Mona Lisa's smile

      a group of politicians

      the moment when you realise that Santa is not real

      the cat's ability to land on its feet

Name five consequences of:

      finding intelligent life on Mars

      compulsory national service

      the world's deserts turning to lakes

      no more human babies being born

      people being born old and growing younger

Five-minute wonders

Teams have five minutes to:

Use newspaper and sticky tape to turn one team member into:

  a Christmas tree

  an Egyptian mummy

  a spaceship

  a micro-organism

  a knight in armour

Name ten:

  sounds no-one can ever hear

  things no-one could ever see on TV

  things no-one could ever hold

  ideas no-one could ever think

  smells that don't exist anymore

  words that no-one understands

  things that everyone doubts

  facts your teachers/parents/children don't know

  mistakes worth making

Explain ten things that:

  ants know about humans

  whales sing about

  cats know about dogs

Give five reasons why:

  green is green

  pirate flags feature a skull and crossbones

  the white Microsoft hand doesn't have a body

The Challenges

problem-solving

creativity

teamwork

cooperation

performance skills

strategic thinking

general knowledge

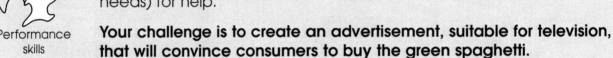

Green spaghetti

Teamwork

Creativity

Performance skills

Materials

a food tin with the label removed, paper, pencils or pens, a timer

The challenge

A disaster has occurred at the local spaghetti factory: somehow harmless green dye has found its way into thousands of tins of spaghetti just like the tin in front of you. Facing bankruptcy if unable to sell the green spaghetti, the manager of the factory has approached your team (already famous for creating hugely successful advertisements for things that no-one really wants or needs) for help.

Your challenge is to create an advertisement, suitable for television, that will convince consumers to buy the green spaghetti.

You will have 10 minutes to prepare your advertisement. A warning will be given after 9 minutes.

You will have 1 minute to perform the advertisement for the judges.

You will be scored as follows:

Teamwork during preparation and performance:	up to 20 points
Creativity of reasons why consumers should buy the green spaghetti:	up to 20 points
Entertainment value of the advertisement:	up to 10 points

Here is the challenge again. (Repeat challenge.)

Your time starts now.

Score Sheet

Green spaghetti	Teamwork 20 points	Creativity of reasons consumers should buy green spaghetti 20 points	Entertainment value of advertisement 10 points	Total	Comments
Teams					
1					
2					
3					
4					
5					
6					

Future features

Teamwork

Creativity

General knowledge

Performance skills

Materials

pencils or pens, paper, a timer

The challenge

The date is 2099. The scene is an ordinary house in your town. Family members, friends and strangers go about living an ordinary day.

Your challenge is to act out what life in this ordinary house is like in 2099.

You must convince the judges that this really is 2099 by what you say, what you do and what happens in your play.

You will have 10 minutes to prepare and practise with a warning given after 9 minutes. Your performance may last for up to 3 minutes.

You will be scored as follows:

Teamwork:	up to 20 points
Creative and convincing portrayal of life in 2099:	up to 25 points
Performance skills:	up to 5 points

Here is the challenge again. (Repeat challenge.)

Your time starts now.

Score Sheet

Future features

Teams	Teamwork 20 points	Creative & convincing portrayal of life in 2099 25 points	Performance skills 5 points	Total	Comments
1					
2					
3					
4					
5					
6					

Sounds on the brink

Teamwork

Creativity

General knowledge

Materials

pencils or pens, paper, a timer

The challenge

Extinction – the end of the line. Millions of species of plant and animal have come and gone and will never be again. Ways of life, trades and technology have disappeared. But what about sounds? There are sounds that once echoed around the planet that are no more. The sound of the last block being lifted into position on the last pyramid, the sound of Julius Caesar's voice, the hiss of the asp that killed Cleopatra, the sound a dodo made as it settled on its egg.

Even today there are sounds – both familiar and rare – that are on the brink of extinction.

Your challenge is to generate a list of sounds that are still heard in the world now but are in danger of becoming extinct.

You will have 10 minutes to prepare a neatly written list of endangered sounds. A warning will be given after 9 minutes.

At the end of the preparation time one person must hand the list to the judges.

You will be scored as follows:	
Teamwork:	up to 10 points
Standard sounds:	1 point each
Clever or creative sounds:	5 points each

Here is the challenge again. (Repeat challenge.)

Your time starts now.

Score Sheet

Sounds on the brink

Teams	Teamwork 10 points	Standard sounds 1 point each	Creative or clever sounds 5 points each	Total	Comments
1					
2					
3					
4					
5					
6					

Puppetry of the feet

Teamwork

Creativity

Performance skills

Construction skills

Materials

thick, non–permanent black, blue and red felt-tipped pens; an assortment of fabric scraps; rubber bands; plastic bags; pieces of cardboard; balloons; a stapler; sticky tape; scissors; pencils or pens; paper; a timer

The challenge

You may have seen or made sock puppets or finger puppets. Today you are going to use the soles of your feet as puppets.

Your challenge is to create and perform a foot-puppet play. The plot must feature a villain, a song and a rowing boat.

You will have 10 minutes to prepare your play. A warning will be given after 9 minutes. You will have 2 minutes to perform the play for the judges.

The puppets are to be created from the soles of your feet and whichever of the materials provided you would like to use.

Each person on your team must have at least 1 foot perform in the play.

You will be scored as follows:

Teamwork during preparation and performance:	up to 20 points
Creativity and entertainment value of the play:	up to 20 points
Effective use of feet as puppets:	up to 10 points

Here is the challenge again. (Repeat challenge.)

Your time starts now.

Score Sheet

Puppetry of the feet

Teams	Teamwork\n\n20 points	Creativity & entertainment value\n\n20 points	Effective use of feet as puppets\n\n10 points	Total	Comments
1					
2					
3					
4					
5					
6					

Pharaoh Joe

Teamwork

Creativity

General knowledge

Materials

pencils or pens, paper, a timer

The challenge

Judge 1:   It is 2000 BC and Pharaoh Joe is beginning to think about his mortality and his body's final earthly resting place. His ancestors have all done the pyramid thing. He looks around – pyramids, pyramids, pyramids!

Judge 2:   I want something different!

Judge 1:   … screams Pharaoh Joe.

Judge 2:   It's got to be big! It's got to be awesome! It's got to be magnificent and eternal and stylish just like me – but NOT a pyramid!

Judge 1:   Pharaoh Joe's anxious undertakers come to your team, Wonders of the World 'R' Us, for help.

Your challenge is to design a magnificent but original tomb to house the dead pharaoh.

You will have 10 minutes to discuss and draw your design. A warning will be given at 9 minutes.

You will have 2 minutes to explain your ideas to the judge – Pharaoh Joe.

You will be scored as follows:

Teamwork:	up to 10 points
Originality of tomb's design:	up to 10 points
Awe-inspiring quality of tomb's design:	up to 10 points
Clarity of drawing and explanation of the tomb:	up to 10 points
Creativity of the dramatic presentation of the design to the judges:	up to 10 points

Here is the challenge again. (Repeat challenge.)
Your time starts now.

Score Sheet

Teams	Teamwork 10 points	Originality of tomb's design 10 points	Awe-inspiring quality of tomb's design 10 points	Clarity of drawing & explanation 10 points	Creativity of presentation 10 points	Total	Comments
1							
2							
3							
4							
5							
6							

Pharaoh Joe

How much can a brain hold?

Teamwork

Strategic
thinking

Materials

a copy of word list (Appendix 1, page 96) enlarged to A3 size for each group, pencils or pens, paper, scissors, a timer

The challenge

In front of you is a list of 160 words.

Your challenge is to memorise as many words from the list as possible.

You team will have 5 minutes in which to memorise the words. A warning will be given after 4 minutes.

When time is up, the word list and all written material are to be handed to the judges and you will be given blank sheets of paper.

You will then have 4 minutes to write all the words, clearly and legibly, for the judges. The words do not have to be in order.

You may divide the task up however you wish.

It is not necessary for the entire team to memorise each word.

You may cut the list of words up.

Scissors, pencil and paper have been provided.

You will be scored as follows:	
Teamwork:	up to 10 points
Each word memorised:	1 point
Any word written down that is not on the list:	minus 2 points

Here is the challenge again. (Repeat challenge.)

Your time starts now.

Score Sheet

Teams	Teamwork 10 points	Each word memorised 1 point	Words not on list -2 points each	Total	Comments
1					
2					
3					
4					
5					
6					

How much can a brain hold?

Lipogram

Teamwork

Creativity

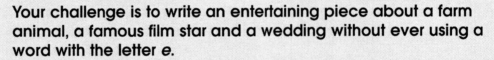

General knowledge

Materials

paper, pencils, a timer

The challenge

A lipogram is a piece of writing from which all words containing a particular letter are omitted.

Your challenge is to write an entertaining piece about a farm animal, a famous film star and a wedding without ever using a word with the letter *e*.

Judges will not score words that seem irrelevant to the story or that are incorrectly spelt.

You will have 10 minutes to plan and write your story. A warning will be given after 9 minutes.

When your preparation time is over you must hand the story, neatly written, to the judges.

You will be scored as follows:

Teamwork:	up to 20 points
Every valid word without an *e*:	1 point
Entertainment value of the story:	up to 20 points
Penalty – any word used that contains the letter *e*:	minus 10 points

---

Here is the challenge again. (Repeat challenge.)

Your time starts now.

Score Sheet

Lipogram

Teams	Teamwork 20 points	Every valid word 1 point each	Entertainment value of story 20 point	Penalty for each word containing e –10 points	Total	Comments
1						
2						
3						
4						
5						
6						

The late news

Teamwork

Creativity

General
knowledge

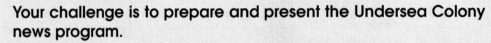

Performance
skills

Materials

pencils or pens, paper, a timer

The challenge

It is 10.00 p.m. on Wednesday, 8 August 2098. The place is Undersea Colony, 20 kilometres below the waves in the centre of the Atlantic Ocean. You are the news crew responsible for the mid-evening local news – 3 minutes of news, sports and weather for the Undersea Colony.

Your challenge is to prepare and present the Undersea Colony news program.

You will have 10 minutes to prepare the program. A warning will be given after 9 minutes.

You will have 3 minutes to present the program.

You will be scored as follows:

Teamwork during preparation and performance:	up to 20 points
Creativity and relevance of your news program to Undersea Colony in 2098:	up to 25 points
Performance skills:	up to 5 points

Here is the challenge again. (Repeat challenge.)

Your time starts now.

Score Sheet

The late news

Teams	Teamwork 20 points	Creativity & relevance of the news to undersea colony 25 points	Performance skills 5 points	Total	Comments
1					
2					
3					
4					
5					
6					

Keep out!

Teamwork

Creativity

General knowledge

Materials

paper, pencils or pens, a timer

The challenge

Hadrian's Wall stretches from sea to sea across northern England. The Emperor Hadrian ordered its construction in AD 122. It was built to keep marauding barbarians out of 'civilised' Roman Britain. Walls are good at keeping things or people in or out but what else keeps things out? An eyelid keeps out the light, a warning sign might keep out intruders and 'turning a blind eye' keeps out reality.

Your challenge is to come up with as many things as you can that keep something or someone out.

You will have 2 minutes' discussion and preparation time.

You may write down ideas if you wish but no paperwork may be used during response time.

At the end of 2 minutes all writing and discussion must cease and paperwork put aside.

You must then face the judges and give examples, one at a time, around the circle, with no passing or prompting, of things that keep something or someone out.

You will have 5 minutes to present your ideas to the judges.

Repetitious answers will not score any points.

You will be scored as follows:

Teamwork during discussion time:	up to 10 points
Standard responses:	1 point each
Creative or clever responses:	5 points each

Here is the challenge again. (Repeat challenge.)

Your time starts now.

Score Sheet

Teams	Teamwork 10 points	Standard responses 1 point each	Creative or clever responses 5 points each	Total	Comments
1					
2					
3					
4					
5					
6					

Keep out!

Jigsaw

Teamwork

Strategic thinking

Materials

a jigsaw puzzle (100 pieces for children, 200 pieces for adults), a flat surface to work on, a timer

The challenge

Your challenge is to assemble as much of this jigsaw as you can in the time allowed.

You will have 5 minutes to put together as many pieces as you can. A warning will be given after 4 minutes.

All pieces must be joined to the one mass to be scored. If there are two or more unconnected masses when time is up, only the larger mass will be scored.

You will be scored as follows:	
Teamwork and cooperation:	20 points
Each piece connected to the main mass:	1 point

Here is the challenge again. (Repeat challenge.)

Your time starts now.

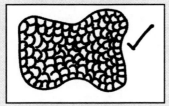 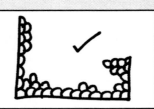 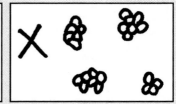

Score Sheet

Jigsaw

Teams	Teamwork 20 points	Pieces joined to main mass 1 point each	Total	Comments
1				
2				
3				
4				
5				
6				

Cinderella's suitcase

Teamwork

Creativity

General knowledge

Construction skills

Materials

a suitcase, a newspaper, a stapler, sticky tape, a pair of scissors, a timer

The challenge

Imagine what a difference it would have made to Humpty Dumpty if all the King's horses and all the King's men had carried some super glue with them. The Gingerbread Man could certainly have used some running shoes and Henny Penny might never have had that fatal meeting with Foxy Loxy if she had been wearing a hard hat. Many of our favourite story characters are just not prepared for what befalls them.

Your challenge is to pack a suitcase with 5 items that would have helped Cinderella through her adventures and explain to the judges how the items would have been of assistance.

You will have 10 minutes to discuss the problem, make the items from the materials provided and pack them into her suitcase. A warning will be given after 9 minutes. When the preparation time is over you will have 2 minutes to explain to the judges how the items would have helped Cinderella.

You will be scored as follows:

Teamwork during preparation and explanation: up to 20 points

Creativity and usefulness of each item to Cinderella: up to 6 points each

---

Here is the challenge again. (Repeat challenge.)

Your time starts now.

Note: Any other well-known storybook character could be substituted for Cinderella.

Score Sheet

Cinderella's suitcase

Teams	Teamwork 20 points	Creativity & usefulness of each item to Cinderella 6 points each					Total	Comments
		Item 1	Item 2	Item 3	Item 4	Item 5		
1								
2								
3								
4								
5								
6								

What is it?

Teamwork

General knowledge

Materials

20 cards face down in a pile, each with the name of an object written on it (book, river, yoyo, cake, canoe, flower, floppy disk, sandcastle, menu, balloon, egg etc.), a timer

The challenge

There are 20 cards in this pile. Each card has an object printed on it. You will take turns to come to the front, take a card, read what is written on it and hand the card to the judges. The rest of the team will try to guess what is written on the card by asking questions. The team member with the card can only answer 'yes' or 'no' to the questions.

Your team's challenge is to guess as many of the objects as you can in the time allowed.

You will have 10 minutes in which to try and guess the objects. A warning will be given after 9 minutes.

Once every team member has had a turn, continue, keeping to the same order.

All questions must be answered with a simple yes or no – any other reply, hand signals, gesturing or acting out will forfeit points at the judges' discretion.

You will be scored as follows:	
Teamwork:	up to 10 points
Each object guessed correctly:	5 points

Here is the challenge again. (Repeat challenge.)

Your time starts now.

Note: The cards must be in the same order for each team.

Score Sheet

Teams	Teamwork 10 points	Each object guessed correctly 5 points	Minus penalty points at judges' discretion	Total	Comments
1					
2					
3					
4					
5					
6					

What is it?

Poetry under the microscope

Teamwork

Creativity

General knowledge

Materials

'On the Antiquity of Microbes' written on a sheet of paper, half as many pencils or pens as there are team members, paper, a timer

The challenge

Supposedly, the shortest poem ever written is this, by an anonymous author: *(Show and read aloud)*

<u>On the Antiquity of Microbes</u>

Adam

Had 'em.

Your challenge is to compose other, equally short, rhyming poems.

You will have 10 minutes to compose and write down your poems. A warning will be given at 9 minutes. When time is up you must immediately stop writing and one person must hand the poems to the judges.

Poems must be legibly written.

All poems must have a title. Title length is unlimited.

All poems must rhyme and contain no more than 3 words each.

You will be scored as follows:

Teamwork:	up to 10 points
Standard poems:	2 points each
Creative or clever poems:	5 points each

Here is the challenge again. (Repeat challenge.)

Your time starts now.

Score Sheet

Poetry under the microscope

Teams	Teamwork 10 points	Standard poems 2 points each	Creative or clever poems 5 points each	Total	Comments
1					
2					
3					
4					
5					
6					

Been to the movies?

Teamwork

Materials

pencils, paper, a ruler, a timer. Judges may find it useful to have up-to-date lists of film titles from books or the Internet.

Creativity

General knowledge

The challenge

Two movie fanatics meet on the street. They are good friends but have not been in contact for years. They have spent so much of their lives watching movies that they incorporate movie titles into every sentence they speak.

Your challenge is to write down the dialogue that occurs between the two friends. The dialogue must contain as many movie titles as possible but still make sense.

You will have 10 minutes to prepare the written dialogue. A warning will be given after 9 minutes.

When time is up you must immediately hand the dialogue, neatly written, to the judges.

All movie titles must be clearly underlined.

Movie titles must make sense in the context of the dialogue to score points.

Judges will not score titles that they do not recognise.

You will be scored as follows:

Teamwork:	up to 10 points
Each movie title used:	2 points each
Creativeness of story and incorporation of titles:	up to 20 points

Here is the challenge again. (Repeat challenge.)

Your time starts now.

Score Sheet

Been to the movies?

Teams	Teamwork 10 points	Each movie title used 2 points each	Creativeness of story & incorporation of titles 20 points	Total	Comments
1					
2					
3					
4					
5					
6					

Tower of strength

Teamwork

Strategic thinking

Construction skills

Materials

a packet of marshmallows, 40 toothpicks, pencils or pens, paper, a metre ruler, a timer

The challenge

Your challenge is to create the tallest structure possible from a packet of marshmallows and 40 toothpicks.

You will have 10 minutes to build the tower. A warning will be given after 9 minutes.

You do not have to use all the toothpicks or marshmallows.

When 10 minutes is up every team member must immediately remove their hands from the tower and not touch it again.

The judges will wait 30 seconds and then measure the height of the tower.

You will be scored as follows:	
Teamwork:	up to 20 points
Height of structure:	1 point per centimetre

Here is the challenge again. (Repeat challenge.)

Your time starts now.

Score Sheet

Tower of strength

Teams	Teamwork 20 points	Height of structure 1 point per cm	Total	Comments
1				
2				
3				
4				
5				
6				

Abducted by aliens

Teamwork

Creativity

General
knowledge

Strategic
thinking

Performance
skills

Materials

a timer, paper, pencils

The challenge

Strangely, word has reached the judges that your team has recently been abducted by aliens. Fortunately you have been returned. The judges are very keen to hear about your experiences. They would like to know the whole story of the abduction and what exactly you experienced. The judges are very sceptical, though – the telling of the story will have to be very believable to convince them.

Your challenge is to tell the story of your team's abduction by aliens convincingly to the judges.

You will have 10 minutes to prepare your story. A warning will be given after 9 minutes. You will have 3 minutes to tell your story to the judges.

During the telling of your story, the judges will not speak to or encourage you in any way.

You will be scored as follows:

Teamwork during preparation and performance:	up to 20 points
Creativity of the story:	up to 20 points
Performance skills that make the story convincing:	up to 10 points

---

Here is the challenge again. (Repeat challenge.)

Your time starts now.

Score Sheet

Abducted by aliens

Teams	Teamwork 20 points	Creativity of story 20 points	Performance skills that make the story convincing 10 points	Total	Comments
1					
2					
3					
4					
5					
6					

Constellation consternation

Teamwork

Creativity

General
knowledge

Materials

a star chart (Appendix 2, page 97), paper, pens or pencils, a timer

The challenge

For thousands of years Earthlings have gazed up at the Southern Cross, Orion's Belt and other distinctive constellations. It is the year 3030. Earth Alliance has just discovered another galaxy five billion light years away. A chart of major star constellations of this galaxy has been brought to your office and is now in front of you: your team is responsible for naming all of Earth Alliance's new discoveries. Earth Alliance has directed that all the new constellations in this galaxy should be named after important events in Earth's history. An example would be 8 stars in the shape of an atomic mushroom cloud named 'Hiroshima Constellation'.

Your challenge is to identify 4 new constellations in the star chart. You must join the stars in each constellation with lines to make them easy to recognise and name them after important events in Earth's history.

You will have 10 minutes to identify and name the constellations. A warning will be given after 9 minutes.

Your team will then be given 1 minute to explain the 4 new constellations to the judges.

You will be scored as follows:

Teamwork: up to 10 points

Creative and relevant
naming of each
constellation: up to 10 points per constellation

Here is the challenge again. (Repeat challenge.)

Your time starts now.

Score Sheet

Constellation consternation

Teams	Teamwork	Creative & relevant naming of each constellation				Total	Comments
	10 points	10 points each					
		1	2	3	4		
1							
2							
3							
4							
5							
6							

If these could speak

Teamwork

Creativity

General knowledge

Performance skills

Materials

3 'artefacts' (for example a *Monopoly* board, a photo of an unusual-looking pop star such as Ozzy Osbourne or Marilyn Manson, a computer mouse pad), a timer

The challenge

It is the year 7000. Nearly 5000 years have elapsed since the Disaster that almost obliterated life on Earth. In the Disaster all records, buildings, technology, art and artefacts were destroyed. No-one in 7000 has any idea what life was like in the time before the Disaster. Now, miraculously, buried deep in 5000-year-old subterranean rubble, 3 curious objects have been discovered. You are the team of archaeologists who have made the discovery and you realise immediately that these objects, whatever they are, hold the key to understanding what civilisation was like at the beginning of the 21st century.

Your challenge is to be the team of archaeologists and explain to the public – in this case the judges – what these objects are and what they reveal about life as it was at the beginning of the 21st century.

You will have 10 minutes to prepare your explanation. A warning will be given after 9 minutes.

You will have 2 minutes to explain your ideas to the judge.

You will be scored as follows:

Teamwork during preparation and explanation:	up to 15 points
Creative explanation of what each object reveals about life in the 21st century:	up to 10 points per object
Performance skills:	up to 5 points

Here is the challenge again. (Repeat challenge.)

Your time starts now.

Score Sheet

If these could speak

Teams	Teamwork 15 points	Creative explanation of what each object reveals about life in the 21st century 10 points each			Performance skills 5 points	Total	Comments
		Object 1	Object 2	Object 3			
1							
2							
3							
4							
5							
6							

Movie time

Teamwork

Creativity

Performance skills

Materials

3 large and interesting photos, pencils or pens, paper, a timer

The challenge

The 3 photos in front of you are stills from a new movie.

Your challenge is to decide what the movie is about and where these 3 photos fit into the plot. You must then perform a synopsis (a summary) of the movie.

You will have 10 minutes to prepare your performance. A warning will be given at 9 minutes.

You will have 2 minutes to perform your short version of the movie.

During your performance you must make it clear to the judges where the 3 photos fit in.

You will be scored as follows:	
Teamwork:	up to 20 points
Creativity of the plot:	up to 20 points
Performance skills:	up to 10 points

Here is the challenge again. (Repeat challenge.)

Your time starts now.

Score Sheet

Movie time	Teams	Teamwork 20 points	Creativity of the plot 20 points	Performance skills 10 points	Total	Comments
	1					
	2					
	3					
	4					
	5					
	6					

Symbols

Teamwork

Creativity

General knowledge

Materials

8 everyday objects (balloon, hat, scissors, calculator, eraser, tea bag, rock, egg etc.), a timer

The challenge

In this world we are familiar with many symbols – a heart means love, a dove symbolises peace, a skull and crossbones tell us that something is poisonous.

There are 8 objects in front of you. Four of these objects symbolise major problems that exist in the world today, the other 4 symbolise possible solutions to these problems.

Your challenge is to explain to the judge what these problems and solutions are and how these objects symbolise them.

You will have 10 minutes to prepare your explanation. A warning will be given after 9 minutes.

You will have 2 minutes to explain your ideas to the judge.

You will be scored as follows:

Teamwork during preparation and presentation: up to 10 points

Creative choice of problems and solutions, and effective symbolism: up to 5 points per object

---

Here is the challenge again. (Repeat challenge.)

Your time starts now.

Score Sheet

Teams	Teamwork 10 points	Objects 5 points each								Total	Comments
		1	2	3	4	5	6	7	8		
1											
2											
3											
4											
5											
6											

You know who

Teamwork

General knowledge

Materials

a pile (face down) of approximately 30 cards with the name of a notable person or character written on each (names should be recognised by teams, so should not be too obscure), a timer, a handbell

The challenge

Here, on the judges' desk, are 30 cards. On each card is the name of a well-known person or character. Some are dead, some living, some have existed only in fiction, film or legend.

Your challenge is to guess as many of these names as possible in the time allowed.

A member of your team will come to the front, read the top card silently and place it back on the judges' desk. That team member then explains, describes or acts out the person or character on the card. **At no stage can that team member mention or spell out the name or any part of the name that is on the card.** For example if the name 'Queen Elizabeth II' was on a card the word 'queen' could not be used to describe her.

A judge will ring this handbell when the name on the card has been guessed correctly. At that point the first team member can sit down and the next team member takes their place and reads the top card. When you have each had a turn, start over again in the same order.

Speed is crucial. You will have 5 minutes to guess the names. A warning will be given at 4 minutes.

You will be scored as follows:	
Teamwork:	up to 10 points
Each name correctly guessed:	5 points

Here is the challenge again. (Repeat challenge.)

Your time starts now.

Note: The cards must be in the same order for each team.

Score Sheet

Teams	Teamwork 10 points	Each name correctly guessed 5 points	Total	Comments
1				
2				
3				
4				
5				
6				

You know who

Who's got mail?

Teamwork

Creativity

General knowledge

Strategic thinking

Construction skills

Materials

a newspaper (identical for each team), glue, several pairs of scissors, a sheet of A4 paper, pencils or pens, a timer

The challenge

Someone from a well-known nursery rhyme or fairytale has written or received a letter. The letter is relevant to that character's story or rhyme. For example Little Red Riding Hood might write a letter to Grandma warning her not to open the door to strangers.

Your challenge is to construct a letter by cutting and gluing words from this newspaper.

You will have 10 minutes to construct and glue down your message with a warning given after 9 minutes.

At the end of 10 minutes the message must be handed to the judges.

You cannot spell out the words one letter at a time – you must use whole words.

You may add 2 handwritten words.

Only words glued to the paper at the end of that time will be judged.

You will be scored as follows:

Teamwork:	up to 20 points
Creativity and relevance of your letter to the chosen rhyme or tale:	up to 30 points

---

Here is the challenge again. (Repeat challenge.)

Your time starts now.

Score Sheet

Who's got mail?

Teams	Teamwork 20 points	Creativity & relevance 30 points	Total	Comments
1				
2				
3				
4				
5				
6				

See no evil

Teamwork

Creativity

General knowledge

Materials

pencils or pens, paper, a timer

The challenge

Imagine that human beings have no eyes. How would this have affected the history of humankind? How would life be different now? What consequences might this lack of eyes have for the future?

Your challenge is to give to the judges as many examples as you can of how the past, present and future would be different if humans had no eyes.

You will have 2 minutes' discussion and preparation time.

You may write down ideas if you wish but no paperwork may be used during response time.

At the end of the 2 minutes all writing and discussion must cease and paperwork put aside.

You must then face the judges and give examples, one at a time, around the circle, with no passing or prompting.

You will have 5 minutes to present your ideas.

You will be scored as follows:	
Teamwork during preparation time:	up to 20 points
Standard responses:	1 point each
Creative or clever responses:	5 points each

Here is the challenge again. (Repeat challenge.)

Your time starts now.

Score Sheet

See no evil

Teams	Teamwork 20 points	Standard responses 1 point each	Creative or clever responses 5 points each	Total	Comments
1					
2					
3					
4					
5					
6					

Scrabble scramble

Teamwork

Strategic thinking

Materials

a *Scrabble* board and letter tiles, a timer

The challenge

You may have played *Scrabble* before but today you will use the *Scrabble* board and letters to test how quickly and effectively your team can work. Cooperation is vital.

Your team's challenge is to make as many words as you can in 5 minutes using these *Scrabble* tiles and board.

You will have 5 minutes to form words with a warning given after 4 minutes. When the judges announce that time is up all hands must be removed from the board immediately.

As in a real game of *Scrabble,* proper nouns, foreign words and abbreviations are not permitted.

Each word must be connected to the main body of words to be scored.

Incomplete or misspelled words will not be scored.

Unlike a real game of *Scrabble* it is not necessary to take turns.

You will be scored as follows:	
Teamwork and cooperation:	up to 25 points
Every letter in a valid word:	1 point

Here is the challenge again. (Repeat challenge.)

Your time starts now.

Score Sheet

Scrabble scramble

Teams	Teamwork & cooperation 25 points	Letters in valid & connected words 1 point each	Total	Comments
1				
2				
3				
4				
5				
6				

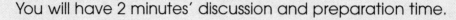

Hands up!

Teamwork

Creativity

General
knowledge

Materials

paper, pencils or pens, a timer

The challenge

Your challenge is to name as many words or expressions as you can that contain the word *hand*.

You will have 2 minutes' discussion and preparation time.

You may write ideas down if you wish but no paperwork may be used during response time.

At the end of 2 minutes all discussion and writing must cease and paperwork put aside.

You will be given 5 minutes to give your responses, one at a time, around the circle with no passing or prompting.

You will be scored as follows:

Teamwork during preparation:	up to 20 points
Standard answers, for example *backhand*:	1 point each
Creative or clever answers:	5 points each

Here is the challenge again. (Repeat challenge.)

Your time starts now.

Score Sheet

Teams	Teamwork 20 points	Standard answers 1 point each	Creative or clever answers 5 points each	Total	Comments
1					
2					
3					
4					
5					
6					

Hands up!

Mars song

Materials

paper, pencils or pens, a timer

Teamwork

Creativity

The challenge

It is the year 2099 and the first Australian colony on Mars is celebrating its tenth anniversary. To mark this joyous occasion the Mars Civic and Cultural Committee has approached your team to compose a patriotic song suitable for the occasion. They want a song that will not only pay tribute to the wonders of their new home but also remind the citizens of Mars Colony of their links to Australia. The Mars Civic and Cultural Committee insists that the song be set to that famous Australian tune, 'Waltzing Matilda'.

General
knowledge

Your challenge is to compose and sing a song suitable for the tenth anniversary of the Australian colony on Mars.

You will have 10 minutes to compose and practise your song. A warning will be given after 9 minutes.

You will have 2 minutes in which to sing the song for the judges.

Every team member must take part in the singing.

Performance
skills

You will be scored as follows:	
Teamwork:	up to 20 points
Creativity of the song and its relevance to both Mars Colony and Australia:	up to 20 points
Performance skills:	up to 10 points

Here is the challenge again. (Repeat challenge.)

Your time starts now.

Score Sheet

Mars song

Teams	Teamwork 20 points	Creativity & relevance 20 points	Performance skills 10 points	Total	Comments
1					
2					
3					
4					
5					
6					

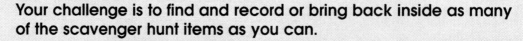

Scavenger hunt

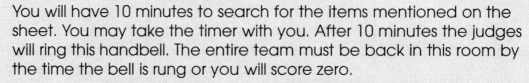

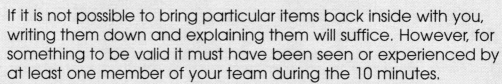

Teamwork

Creativity

General knowledge

Strategic thinking

Materials

a copy per group of scavenger hunt questions (Appendix 3, page 98) enlarged to A3 size, pencils or pens, a timer, a handbell

The challenge

On the desk in front of you is a list of 10 things to find in a scavenger hunt.

Your challenge is to find and record or bring back inside as many of the scavenger hunt items as you can.

You will have 10 minutes to search for the items mentioned on the sheet. You may take the timer with you. After 10 minutes the judges will ring this handbell. The entire team must be back in this room by the time the bell is rung or you will score zero.

If it is not possible to bring particular items back inside with you, writing them down and explaining them will suffice. However, for something to be valid it must have been seen or experienced by at least one member of your team during the 10 minutes.

You will have 3 minutes to explain your answers to the judges.

You will be scored as follows:

Teamwork:	up to 10 points
Satisfactory answers to each scavenger hunt problem:	2 points each
Creative or clever answers to each scavenger hunt problem:	5 points each

---

Here is the challenge again. (Repeat challenge.)

Your time starts now.

Note: Depending on your circumstances, you may need to specify where the teams can search, out-of-bounds areas etc.

Score Sheet

Scavenger hunt

Teams	Teamwork 10 points	Satisfactory answer to a problem 2 points each	Creative or clever answer to a problem 5 points each	Total	Comments
1					
2					
3					
4					
5					
6					

In the picture

Teamwork

Creativity

Performance
skills

Materials

an unusual photo or artwork that portrays a group of people doing something obscure (for example *The Oath of the Horatti* by Jacques-Louis David, *Netherlandish Proverbs* by Pieter Bruegel or *The Dance of Life* by Edvard Munch), pencils or pens, paper, a timer

The challenge

Who are these people? Where are they? What are they doing? What interesting things are about to happen?

Your challenge is to put yourselves in the place of the people in the photo then 'come to life' and act out what happens next.

You will have 10 minutes to discuss the photo and prepare your performance. A warning will be given after 9 minutes.

At the end of 10 minutes your performance will begin with the team 'frozen' in place as in the picture.

Your performance may be up to 2 minutes in length.

You will be scored as follows:

Teamwork during preparation and performance:	up to 20 points
Creativity of ideas:	up to 20 points
Performance skills:	up to 10 points

Here is the challenge again. (Repeat challenge.)

Your time starts now.

Note: The number of people in the picture should be equal to or greater than the number of people in each team.

Score Sheet

Teams	Teamwork 20 points	Creativity of ideas 20 points	Performance skills 10 points	Total	Comments
1					
2					
3					
4					
5					
6					

Light my fire

Teamwork

Creativity

General knowledge

Materials

pencils or pens, paper, a timer

The challenge

The climax of the opening ceremony of every Olympic Games is the moment when the Olympic Torch enters the arena and the flame is lit – a fire to last for the duration of the Games and then finally to be passed on to the next nation to host the spectacular sporting event.

Over the years, Olympic organising committees have found imaginative and spectacular ways to light the flame. For example, at Barcelona a fiery arrow was shot across the sky to ignite the flame.

It is difficult coming up with bigger and better ideas so the organising committee of the next Olympic Games has asked your team to help.

Your challenge is to come up with 3 really spectacular, original and crowd-pleasing ways to light the Olympic flame.

You will have 10 minutes to prepare your ideas. A warning will be given after 9 minutes. You will have 2 minutes to explain your ideas to the judges.

You will be scored as follows:

Teamwork:	up to 20 points
Creativity of ideas for lighting the flame:	up to 10 points for each idea

---

Here is the challenge again. (Repeat challenge.)

Your time starts now.

Score Sheet

Light my fire

Teams	Teamwork 20 points	1st idea 10 points	2nd idea 10 points	3rd idea 10 points	Total	Comments
1						
2						
3						
4						
5						
6						

Tall Stories

Teamwork

Creativity

Strategic thinking

Construction skills

Materials

10 sheets of newspaper, 10 paperclips, a timer

The challenge

Your challenge is to construct the tallest self-supporting structure that you can from these 10 sheets of newspaper and paperclips.

You will have 6 minutes to construct the structure. A warning will be given at 5 minutes.

When the judges announce that time is up, all hands must be removed immediately from the structure.

The judges will wait 30 seconds and then measure the height of the structure.

You will be scored as follows:	
Teamwork:	up to 20 points
Height of structure:	1 point per centimetre

Here is the challenge again. (Repeat challenge.)

Your time starts now.

Score Sheet

Tall stories

Teams	Teamwork 20 points	Height of structure 1 point per cm	Total	Comments
1				
2				
3				
4				
5				
6				

The cloning catastrophe

Teamwork

Creativity

General
knowledge

Performance
skills

Materials

pencils or pens, paper, a timer

The challenge

It is the year 2020 and a group of scientists have finally succeeded in cloning an extinct animal. However, something has gone terribly wrong.

Your challenge is to create a 2-minute television news story about the cloning catastrophe.

You will have 10 minutes to prepare your news report. A warning will be given after 9 minutes.

You will be scored as follows:

Teamwork during preparation and performance:	up to 20 points
Creativity of the story:	up to 20 points
Performance skills:	up to 10 points

Here is the challenge again. (Repeat challenge.)

Your time starts now.

Score Sheet

The cloning catastrophe

Teams	Teamwork 20 points	Creativity of the story 20 points	Performance skills 10 points	Total	Comments
1					
2					
3					
4					
5					
6					

Camera obscura

Teamwork

Creativity

General knowledge

Materials

a strange or interesting photo (either 1 large copy or several smaller copies), pencils or pens, paper, a timer

The challenge

You have in front of you a very unusual picture.

Your challenge is to make up 5 titles for this photo.

You will have 10 minutes to discuss ideas and write down the 5 titles.

A warning will be given after 9 minutes.

At the end of 10 minutes you must hand your titles to the judges.

You will be scored as follows:

Teamwork:	up to 15 points
Creativity of each title:	up to 7 points per title

Here is the challenge again. (Repeat challenge.)

Your time starts now.

Score Sheet

Teams	Teamwork 15 points	Title 1 7 points	Title 2 7 points	Title 3 7 points	Title 4 7 points	Title 5 7 points	Total	Comments
1								
2								
3								
4								
5								
6								

Camera obscura

Bunyip trap

Teamwork

Creativity

Construction
skills

Materials

an envelope, a rubber band, a toothbrush, 3 icy-pole sticks, sticky tape, a page from a newspaper, an item of dolls' clothing, a 20-cm piece of string, a timer

The challenge

The sleepless residents of Enmarellabella are being kept awake by a bunyip that creeps into their yards at night. The bunyip howls bloodcurdling howls and often steals washing off their clotheslines. The troublesome beast then dresses up in the stolen clothes and makes frightening faces at their windows.

The bunyip is an endangered species, of course, and must not be harmed in any way. So the residents of Enmarellabella have approached your team in the hope that you can devise a trap to capture the bunyip.

Your challenge is to make a model of an effective bunyip trap from the materials provided and explain to the judges how such a trap would capture this particular bunyip.

You will have 10 minutes to design and make the trap. A warning will be given after 9 minutes.

You will have 2 minutes to explain to the judges how the trap works.

You will be scored as follows:

Teamwork during preparation and explanation of the trap:	up to 20 points
Creativity of the design of the trap:	up to 15 points
Effectiveness of the design of the trap:	up to 15 points

Here is the challenge again. (Repeat challenge.)

Your time starts now.

Score Sheet

Teams	Teamwork 20 points	Creativity of the design 15 points	Effectiveness of the design 15 points	Total	Comments
1					
2					
3					
4					
5					
6					

Bunyip trap

Dead ball fall

Teamwork

Creativity

Strategic
thinking

Construction
skills

Materials

a tennis ball, A4 paper, straws, scissors, masking tape, a 2-metre measuring tape, 2 circles marked on floor (see Appendix 4, page 99 for diagram), a timer

The challenge

Tennis balls are meant to bounce, right? Not this time!

Your challenge is to construct a frame for a tennis ball that will prevent it bouncing or rolling away when it hits the floor.

You have been given 2 sheets of A4 paper, 2 straws, scissors and 20 centimetres of masking tape to use.

You will have 10 minutes to construct and trial your container. You will be given a warning at 9 minutes.

When the judges indicate they are ready, one team member must drop the frame with the ball inside from exactly 2 metres above the centre of the circle.

The closer your ball is to the centre of the circle when it stops moving, the more points you will score.

You will be scored as follows:

Teamwork:	up to 20 points
The ball remains wholly within the inner circle:	120 points
The ball stops within the outer circle, but outside the inner circle:	1 point for every cm from outer circle
The ball stops moving outside the outer circle:	0 points

Here is the challenge again. (Repeat challenge.)

Your time starts now.

Score Sheet

Dead ball fall

Teams	Teamwork 20 points	Ball stopped moving wholly within inner circle 120 points	or	Distance from outer circle to ball 1 cm = 1 point	or	Ball stopped moving beyond outer circle 0 points	Total	Comments
1								
2								
3								
4								
5								
6								

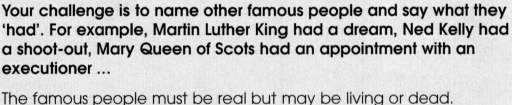

What they had

Teamwork

Creativity

General
knowledge

Strategic
thinking

Materials

pencils or pens, paper, a timer

The challenge

Martin Luther King, the leader of the civil rights movement in the United States of America in the 1950s and 60s, made a famous speech that began, 'I have a dream …'

Your challenge is to name other famous people and say what they 'had'. For example, Martin Luther King had a dream, Ned Kelly had a shoot-out, Mary Queen of Scots had an appointment with an executioner …

The famous people must be real but may be living or dead.

You will have 2 minutes' discussion and preparation time.

You may write down ideas if you wish but no paperwork may be used during response time.

At the end of 2 minutes all writing and discussion must cease and paperwork put aside.

You must then face the judges and give examples, one at a time, around the circle, with no passing or prompting.

You will have 5 minutes to present your ideas.

You will be scored as follows:

Teamwork during discussion time:	up to 10 points
Standard responses:	1 point each
Creative or clever responses:	3 points each

Here is the challenge again. (Repeat challenge.)

Your time starts now.

Score Sheet

What they had	Teams	Teamwork Up to 10 points	Standard answers 1 point each	Creative or clever answers 3 points each	Total	Comments
	1					
	2					
	3					
	4					
	5					
	6					

Olympic sport

Teamwork

Creativity

General knowledge

Performance skills

Materials

a few metres of string, 2 balloons, a broom handle, a hoop, newspaper, a box, an indoor ball, scissors, tape, a chair, pencils or pens, paper, a timer

The challenge

A surprise announcement has just been made – the 2012 Olympics are going to be held right here in your town. The organising committee of the Olympics has been asked to trial a brand new Australian sport at the Games and has come to your team for ideas. The Committee believes that because this is an Australian Olympics, the sport should be based on our most well-known song, 'Waltzing Matilda'.

Your challenge is to invent, describe and demonstrate to the organising committee (in this case the judges) a new Australian sport based on 'Waltzing Matilda'.

You may use any or all of the materials supplied.

You will have 10 minutes to prepare your presentation. A warning will be given after 9 minutes.

You will have 2 minutes' performance time to describe and demonstrate your sport to the judges.

You will be scored as follows:

Teamwork during preparation and presentation:	up to 15 points
Originality of the sport:	up to 15 points
Relevance of the sport to 'Waltzing Matilda':	up to 15 points
Performance skills:	up to 5 points

Here is the challenge again. (Repeat challenge.)

Your time starts now.

Score Sheet

Teams	Teamwork 15 points	Originality of sport 15 points	Relevance to 'Waltzing Matilda' 15 points	Performance skills 5 points	Total	Comments
1						
2						
3						
4						
5						
6						

Crossword

Teamwork

General knowledge

Strategic thinking

Materials

enlarged copies of crossword grid (Appendix 5, page 100), dark-lead pencils, an eraser, a timer

The challenge

In front of you is a crossword grid – an unusual crossword grid, however, as there are no clues to solve.

Your challenge is to fill the crossword grid with as many words as you can in the time allowed.

You will have 5 minutes to complete as much of the grid as you can. A warning will be given after 4 minutes.

You must start at the square marked with a star, write a word and then connect words to that word and so on. When time is up, only words connected to this main body of words will score.

No proper nouns or foreign words are permitted; however, you may use the same word more than once.

Only correctly spelt words will score.

You will be scored as follows:

Teamwork:	up to 20 points
Words:	2 points each

Here is the challenge again. (Repeat challenge.)

Your time starts now.

Score Sheet

Crossword

Teams	Teamwork 20 points	Valid words 2 points each	Total	Comments
1				
2				
3				
4				
5				
6				

Body music

Teamwork

Creativity

Performance skills

Materials

pens or pencils, paper, a timer

The challenge

Music – those interesting and pleasant sounds that people have been making since the dawn of humankind. We have made music to entertain, express feelings and ideas and, sometimes, to tell stories.

Your challenge is to create and perform a piece of music using only your bodies and voices as instruments. The piece of music should tell the story of something that occurs in nature.

You will have 10 minutes to prepare your piece of music. A warning will be given after 9 minutes.

When the preparation time is up you will be given 1 minute to explain the story to the judges and then 2 minutes to perform the music.

Please note that while voices are permitted in the music, no actual words are to be used and speaking is not permitted during the performance of the music.

You will be scored as follows:

Teamwork during preparation and performance: up to 20 points

Creativity of the nature-story told in the music: up to 15 points

Effective use of bodies and voices as instruments: up to 15 points

---

Here is the challenge again. (Repeat challenge.)

Your time starts now.

Score Sheet

Body music

Teams	Teamwork 20 points	Creativity of the nature-story told 15 points	Effective use of bodies and voices as instruments 15 points	Total	Comments
1					
2					
3					
4					
5					
6					

Here lies ...

Teamwork

Creativity

General knowledge

Materials

pencils or pens, paper, a timer

The challenge

An epitaph is a short statement in memory of a dead person. It is often put on a gravestone or tomb. Epitaphs sometimes begin, 'Here lies ...'.

Your challenge is to write 3 epitaphs, one each for Donald Duck, Einstein and Cleopatra.

You will have 10 minutes to compose and write the epitaphs. A warning will be given after 9 minutes.

At the end of that time you must hand the 3 neatly written epitaphs to the judges.

You will be scored as follows:

Teamwork:	up to 20 points
Creativity or cleverness of epitaphs:	up to 10 points each

Here is the challenge again. (Repeat challenge.)

Your time starts now.

Score Sheet

Teams	Teamwork 20 points	Creative or clever epitaphs 10 points each			Total	Comments
		Donald Duck	Einstein	Cleopatra		
1						
2						
3						
4						
5						
6						

The big idea

Teamwork

Creativity

General knowledge

Materials

pencils or pens, paper, a timer

The challenge

Think of New York and the Statue of Liberty comes to mind. Paris – the Eiffel Tower. London – Big Ben. Sydney – the Harbour Bridge and Opera House. These structures are famous, memorable and synonymous with the cities they represent.

Now, your town has decided to build a structure, a monument that will put it on the map; an icon that will symbolise something important about your town; a landmark that will last for generations, attracting tourists and increasing civic pride.

Because of your creative abilities and your extensive local knowledge your team has been chosen to design this new structure.

Your challenge is to prepare a design for a structure that represents something important about your town, something completely original that will attract tourists and make the citizens of your town proud.

You have 10 minutes to prepare your design. A warning will be given after 9 minutes.

You will have 2 minutes to explain your design and the reasons behind your ideas to the judges.

You will be scored as follows:	
Teamwork:	up to 20 points
Creativity of the design:	up to 15 points
Relevance of the design to town:	up to 15 points

Here is the challenge again. (Repeat challenge.)

Your time starts now.

Score Sheet

The big idea					
Teams	Teamwork 20 points	Creativity of design 15 points	Relevance of design to town 15 points	Total	Comments
1					
2					
3					
4					
5					
6					

Appendix 1

How much can a brain hold?

CAR	BASKET	MOSQUITO	HORSE	RUG
TENT	TOY	BED	SOCK	BRIDESMAID
BUTTON	SWING	DRAGON	WAND	SEED
NAIL	PENCIL	GUN	BEAN	WAX
POT	TIN	PIZZA	SOAP	NETTLE
PLANE	CAT	BOOT	BRIDGE	THUNDER
VOLCANO	KEY	PAINTING	FISH	WASP
FIREFIGHTER	ELEPHANT	SAND	STAIRS	TONGUE
ORANGE	TAPE	TICKET	HORIZON	SILK
SOUP	BOOK	MOUSE	GARGOYLE	POLICE
BANDAGE	WINDOW	TRUMPET	LACE	GLOBE
SPOON	GIRL	HELMET	SEAL	TITLE
VAMPIRE	BRICK	FENCE	CHESS PIECE	MIRACLE
CABBAGE	LOLLY	RING	WIRE	LAMP
VEST	DICE	LIGHT	KITTEN	GRAVE
FOSSIL	FEATHER	SHIP	LEG	CANDLE
COUCH	HAND	CHAIR	TIN	BRUSH
HORN	OCTOPUS	BELL	ARROW	ROOM
RABBIT	UMBRELLA	PIN	PLUG	CIRCUS
PLATE	NUMBER	MOUNTAIN	STAIN	WIND
RIBBON	PIPE	CASTLE	PATTERN	ROBE
DAM	VIOLIN	HEART	SPIKE	TEACHER
ROAD	ROOF	LEAF	KNEE	GIFT
BISCUIT	MUSHROOM	NOSE	CLOCK	FLUTE
PILLOW	PUDDLE	VIDEO	POCKET	GASMASK
PLAN	TREE	JIGSAW	CARROT	HAMMER
AXE	BOWL	GLASS	DANCER	BADGE
GOOSE	HANDLE	HOLE	PENGUIN	HARP
DOLLAR	COMPOST	CLOUD	THRONE	STOPWATCH
WHEEL	BAG	UFO	SWORD	PICTURE
CUP	GYPSY	PAPER	HUT	TRUNK
BALL	LOOT	STRING	STAMP	STATUE

Appendix 2
constellation consternation

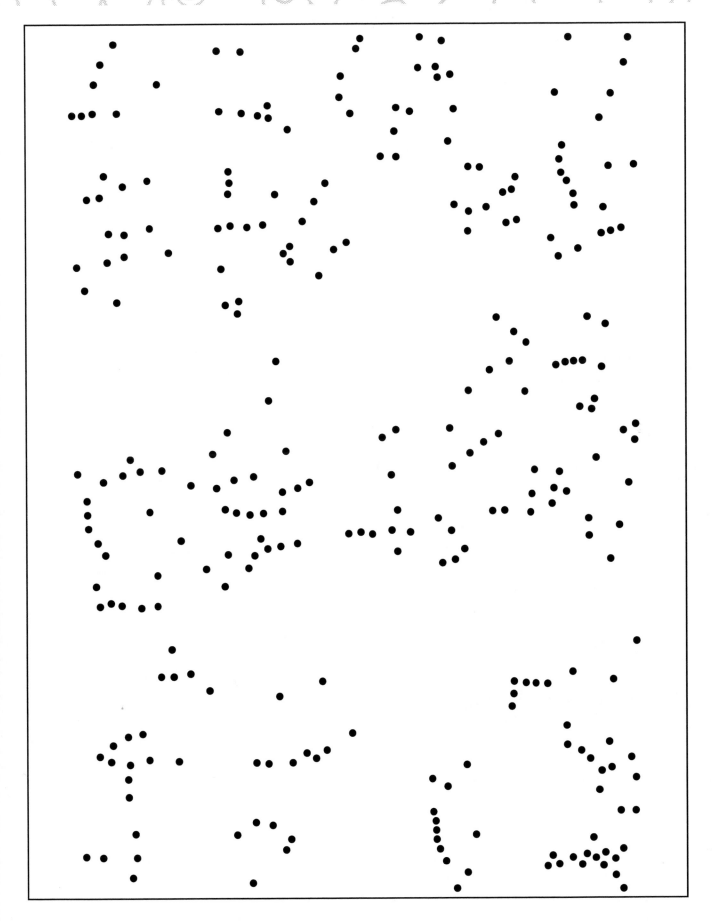

Appendix 3
Scavenger hunt

Team: _____

> You have 10 minutes to find or see the things listed below. If you are unable to bring something inside you may write down what it is. You will need to explain your choices to the judges.

1. Something that no-one in the world can draw.

2. Something that represents hope.

3. Something from the future.

4. Something new.

5. Something infinite.

6. Something that is the opposite of something else.

7. Something made by humans but not used by humans.

8. Something terrifying.

9. Something mentioned in a proverb.

10. An unanswerable question.

Appendix 4

Dead ball fall

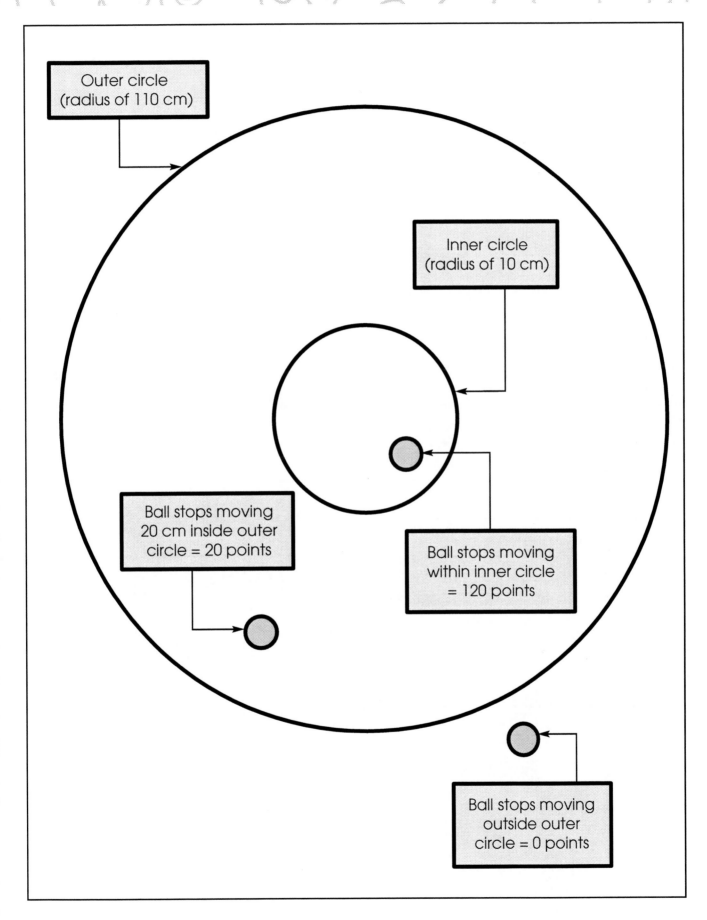

Outer circle
(radius of 110 cm)

Inner circle
(radius of 10 cm)

Ball stops moving
20 cm inside outer
circle = 20 points

Ball stops moving
within inner circle
= 120 points

Ball stops moving
outside outer
circle = 0 points

Appendix 5
Crossword

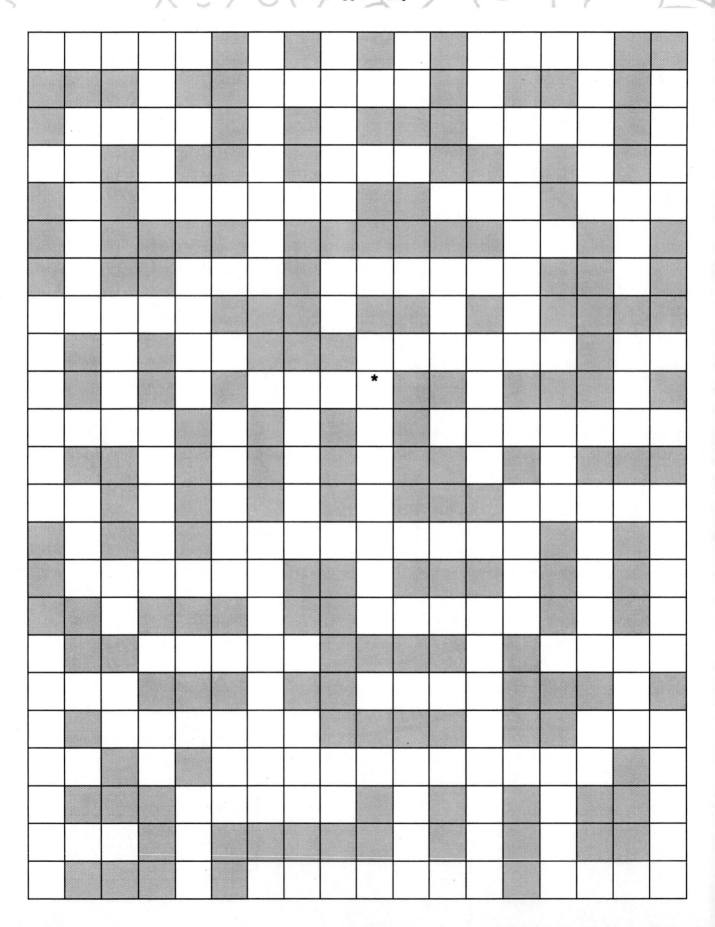